# CGP has it all (net)worked out...

GCSE Computer Science exams are pretty tough — but don't worry, this brilliant CGP book is here to RAM home your revision!

It's packed with 10-Minute Tests covering every OCR topic — ideal for quick bursts of digestible practice.  We've even included mixed-topic tests too for a taste of the real exams.

And with answers for all questions at the back of the book, it'd be a logic error to choose anyone other than CGP!

# CGP — still the best ☺

Our sole aim here at CGP is to produce the highest quality books — carefully written, immaculately presented and dangerously close to being funny.

Then we work our socks off to get them out to you — at the cheapest possible prices.

Published by CGP

Editors:
Liam Dyer, Michael Weynberg

Contributor:
Oliver Kerr

ISBN: 978 1 78908 402 3

With thanks to Shaun Harrogate and Shaun Whorton for the proofreading.
With thanks to Ana Pungartnik for the copyright research.


Printed by Elanders Ltd, Newcastle upon Tyne

Based on the classic CGP style created by Richard Parsons.

# Contents

# Test 1

There are **12 questions** in this test.  Give yourself **10 minutes** to answer them all.

1.  Which of these contains instructions used by the CPU when a computer is booting up?

    **A**   Hard disk drive

    **B**   RAM

    **C**   ROM

    *[1]*

2.  Which part of the CPU performs operations such as AND, OR and NOT?

    **A**   Arithmetic Logic Unit (ALU)

    **B**   Control Unit (CU)

    **C**   Memory Data Register (MDR)

    *[1]*

3.  A device driver is a piece of software which...

    **A**   ... provides a user interface.

    **B**   ... allows an OS to interact with internal hardware or peripherals.

    **C**   ... manages user files and applications.

    *[1]*

4.  Which of the following types of storage media are commonly used by businesses to archive large amounts of data?

    **A**   Hard disk drive

    **B**   Optical disc

    **C**   Magnetic tape

    *[1]*

5.  Processor registers temporarily hold small amounts of data needed by...

    **A**   ... the CPU.

    **B**   ... RAM.

    **C**   ... the hard disk drive.

    *[1]*

6.  Which of these types of storage generally has the highest cost per gigabyte?

    **A**   Solid state drives

    **B**   Hard disk drives

    **C**   Magnetic tape

    *[1]*

7.  True or False?  "In the Von Neumann architecture, the same memory unit is used for data and instructions."

    **A**   True

    **B**   False

    *[1]*

8.  An operating system helps with file management by...

    **A**   ... compressing every file.

    **B**   ... arranging the files into a hierarchical structure.

    *[1]*

**9.** Give an example of a device which is likely to contain an embedded system.

........................................................................................................................................

*[1]*

**10.** Sian uses compression software on a file. Give one benefit of compressing the file.

........................................................................................................................................

........................................................................................................................................

*[1]*

**11.** What is the difference between full and incremental backups?

........................................................................................................................................

........................................................................................................................................

........................................................................................................................................

........................................................................................................................................

*[2]*

**12.** Explain what happens during the 'fetch' stage of the fetch-decode-execute cycle.

........................................................................................................................................

........................................................................................................................................

........................................................................................................................................

........................................................................................................................................

........................................................................................................................................

........................................................................................................................................

*[3]*

15

Section 1: Components of a Computer System

# Test 2

There are **11 questions** in this test. Give yourself **10 minutes** to answer them all.

**1.** ROM is...

   **A** ... volatile.

   **B** ... non-volatile.

*[1]*

**2.** Hard disk drives are a type of...

   **A** ... primary storage.

   **B** ... secondary storage.

   **C** ... tertiary storage.

*[1]*

**3.** True or False? "SSDs experience the same fragmentation problems as HDDs."

   **A** True

   **B** False

*[1]*

**4.** Clock speed is...

   **A** ... the number of instructions that a CPU can process at the same time.

   **B** ... the number of cycles per second that a CPU can carry out.

*[1]*

**5.** Cache memory has...

   **A** ... a large capacity that is slow for the CPU to access.

   **B** ... a large capacity that is quick for the CPU to access.

   **C** ... a small capacity that is quick for the CPU to access.

*[1]*

**6.** RAM is used for...

   **A** ... storing instructions that tell the CPU how to boot up.

   **B** ... archiving information.

   **C** ... storing data, files and programs that are in use.

*[1]*

**7.** Virtual memory is used when...

   **A** ... RAM is full of data.

   **B** ... the hard drive is full of data.

   **C** ... ROM is full of data.

*[1]*

**8.** What type of utility software scrambles data to stop third-parties from accessing it?

   **A** Defragmentation

   **B** Compression

   **C** Encryption

*[1]*

---

Section 1: Components of a Computer System

**9.** What is the purpose of the CPU?

..........................................................................................................................

..........................................................................................................................

*[1]*

**10.** What are two main functions of an operating system?

1. ......................................................................................................................

..........................................................................................................................

2. ......................................................................................................................

..........................................................................................................................

*[2]*

**11.** Greg is building his own PC and is deciding whether to have
a Hard Disk Drive (HDD) or a Solid State Drive (SSD).
Give two advantages and two disadvantages of choosing the SSD instead of the HDD.

Advantages:

1. ......................................................................................................................

..........................................................................................................................

2. ......................................................................................................................

..........................................................................................................................

Disadvantages:

1. ......................................................................................................................

..........................................................................................................................

2. ......................................................................................................................

..........................................................................................................................

*[4]*

15

# Test 3

There are **12 questions** in this test. Give yourself **10 minutes** to answer them all.

1. Which type of user interface requires the most resources to run?

   **A** Command line interface

   **B** Graphical user interface

   *[1]*

2. Embedded systems are designed to...

   **A** ... carry out a single task efficiently.

   **B** ... carry out a variety of tasks.

   *[1]*

3. What type of software allows developers to legally make modifications to its source code?

   **A** Open source

   **B** Proprietary

   *[1]*

4. Which type of storage generally has the fastest read/write speed?

   **A** Memory card

   **B** Optical disc

   **C** Solid state drive

   *[1]*

5. True or False? "The OS gives processes a higher priority for execution by the CPU than others."

   **A** True

   **B** False

   *[1]*

6. Increasing the number of cores in a CPU...

   **A** ... increases the number of instructions processed by each core per second.

   **B** ... increases the number of instructions that can be carried out at the same time.

   *[1]*

7. Which of the following generally uses flash memory?

   **A** ROM chips

   **B** Optical discs

   **C** HDDs

   *[1]*

8. Which of the following components controls the flow of data in the CPU?

   **A** ALU

   **B** OS

   **C** CU

   *[1]*

---

Section 1: Components of a Computer System

9.  How does virtual memory impact a computer's performance?

.........................................................................................................................

.........................................................................................................................

*[1]*

10. What is the function of the accumulator?

.........................................................................................................................

.........................................................................................................................

*[1]*

11. Give two security measures an OS may have to prevent unauthorised access.

1.  ....................................................................................................................

2.  ....................................................................................................................

*[2]*

12. A teacher wants to provide each of their students with some files and
    open-source software, which will take up 6.5 GB of storage space.

    State an appropriate storage device to use.  Give two reasons for your answer.

    Storage device: ...........................................................................................

    1.  ................................................................................................................

    ....................................................................................................................

    2.  ................................................................................................................

    ....................................................................................................................

*[3]*

15

# Test 4

There are **11 questions** in this test. Give yourself **10 minutes** to answer them all.

1. The World Wide Web is based on...

   **A** ... a client-server relationship.

   **B** ... a peer-to-peer relationship.

   *[1]*

2. True or False? "A WAN connects LANs across large geographical distances."

   **A** True

   **B** False

   *[1]*

3. A packet is...

   **A** ... a type of file.

   **B** ... a chunk of data being transmitted over a network.

   **C** ... a transmission protocol.

   *[1]*

4. Which of these pieces of hardware directs packets using IP addresses?

   **A** NIC

   **B** Switch

   **C** Router

   *[1]*

5. How many Virtual Private Networks (VPNs) can exist on one physical network?

   **A** Only one

   **B** More than one

   *[1]*

6. The 2.4 GHz Wi-Fi® frequency band has more overlapping channels than the 5 GHz band. The 2.4 GHz band...

   **A** ... has a shorter range.

   **B** ... experiences more interference.

   *[1]*

7. Which of these protocols would be used to upload a large number of files to a remote server?

   **A** HTTP

   **B** IMAP

   **C** FTP

   *[1]*

8. Which of these is an example of a phishing attack?

   **A** Downloading software containing a virus from the Internet.

   **B** Attempting to gain sensitive information by impersonating a trustworthy person or business.

   **C** Attempting to overload a server to cause it to crash.

   *[1]*

**9.** What is the name of the network topology represented in the diagram on the right?

..................................................

*[1]*

**10.** Cameron uses a weak password on his computer and has not updated his anti-malware software. How could each of his actions put his computer at risk?

..................................................................................................

..................................................................................................

..................................................................................................

..................................................................................................

*[2]*

**11.** Give two advantages and two disadvantages of storing data in the cloud.

Advantages:

1. ...............................................................................................

...............................................................................................

2. ...............................................................................................

...............................................................................................

Disadvantages:

1. ...............................................................................................

...............................................................................................

2. ...............................................................................................

...............................................................................................

*[4]*

15

# Test 5

There are **11 questions** in this test. Give yourself **10 minutes** to answer them all.

1. Which type of cable is best for transmitting data over very large distances without losing signal quality?

   A   Coaxial

   B   Ethernet

   C   Fibre optic

   *[1]*

2. Which of the following examines data entering and leaving a network in order to block any potential threats?

   A   Router

   B   Firewall

   C   Switch

   *[1]*

3. Bandwidth is...

   A   ... the amount of data that can be transferred in a given time.

   B   ... a specific frequency band used by Wi-Fi®.

   *[1]*

4. True or False? "IP addresses are assigned to network-enabled devices by the manufacturer."

   A   True

   B   False

   *[1]*

5. A DNS...

   A   ... assigns a MAC address to each computer on a network.

   B   ... stores domain names and their corresponding IP addresses.

   C   ... is used to create a LAN.

   *[1]*

6. An active attack is when someone...

   A   ... in an organisation exploits their network access for malicious purposes.

   B   ... monitors and intercepts sensitive data being transferred on a network.

   C   ... installs malware on a network with the intent to harm devices.

   *[1]*

7. Which of these protocols is responsible for packet switching on a network?

   A   Internet Protocol (IP)

   B   File Transfer Protocol (FTP)

   C   Hyper Text Transfer Protocol (HTTP)

   *[1]*

8. IMAP is used for...

   A   ... accessing websites.

   B   ... retrieving emails.

   C   ... moving and editing files.

   *[1]*

**9.** What is the purpose of a packet's checksum number?

...........................................................................................................................................

...........................................................................................................................................

[1]

**10.** What are two features of a strong password?

1. ........................................................................................................................................

2. ........................................................................................................................................

[2]

**11.** Two companies are deciding which network model would suit their offices.

| Company A | Company B |
|---|---|
| 200 employees<br>Many IT specialists | 5 employees<br>No IT specialists |

Suggest why a client-server network may be appropriate for Company A.

...........................................................................................................................................

...........................................................................................................................................

...........................................................................................................................................

...........................................................................................................................................

Suggest why a peer-to-peer network may be appropriate for Company B.

...........................................................................................................................................

...........................................................................................................................................

...........................................................................................................................................

...........................................................................................................................................

[4]

15

# Test 6

There are **12 questions** in this test. Give yourself **10 minutes** to answer them all.

**1.** A MAC address...

 **A** ... is assigned to a device when it first accesses a network.

 **B** ... is required for communication between devices on the same network.

*[1]*

**2.** Which of these is likely to have a more stable connection?

 **A** A wired LAN using Ethernet cables.

 **B** A wireless LAN using Wi-Fi®.

*[1]*

**3.** What type of attack exploits weak input validation on a website?

 **A** Phishing

 **B** SQL injection

 **C** Denial of service

*[1]*

**4.** POP3 is a protocol which is used to...

 **A** ... check a packet has arrived at its destination.

 **B** ... access files across a network.

 **C** ... retrieve emails from a server.

*[1]*

**5.** A switch is used to....

 **A** ... transmit data between networks.

 **B** ... scan data for potential threats.

 **C** ... connect devices on a LAN.

*[1]*

**6.** Which security measure is the best defence against a passive attack?

 **A** Data encryption

 **B** User access levels

 **C** Anti-malware software

*[1]*

**7.** Which of the following statements about layers of network protocols is true?

 **A** They discourage developers from creating universal software.

 **B** They break network communication down into manageable chunks.

*[1]*

**8.** A problem with a wired full-mesh network is that...

 **A** ... the whole network is affected if a single device has an issue.

 **B** ... there are lots of data collisions.

 **C** ... the more devices you add, the more expensive it gets to connect them all.

*[1]*

---

**9.** Name the protocol that sends encrypted data between a web server and a web browser.

..................................................................................................................................................

*[1]*

**10.** A good network policy may enforce user access levels. What are user access levels?

..................................................................................................................................................

..................................................................................................................................................

*[1]*

**11.** Explain what is meant by a 'virtual network' and outline how one is created.

..................................................................................................................................................

..................................................................................................................................................

..................................................................................................................................................

..................................................................................................................................................

*[2]*

**12.** Give three reasons why a business may choose to use a LAN instead
of using a number of stand-alone (unconnected) devices.

1. ...........................................................................................................................................

..................................................................................................................................................

2. ...........................................................................................................................................

..................................................................................................................................................

3. ...........................................................................................................................................

..................................................................................................................................................

*[3]*

| 15 |

14

# Test 7

There are **12 questions** in this test. Give yourself **10 minutes** to answer them all.

**1.** True or False? "Peer-to-peer networks do not have a central server."

    **A**   True

    **B**   False

*[1]*

**2.** The Internet is an example of a...

    **A**   ... LAN.

    **B**   ... WAN.

*[1]*

**3.** File hosting is when...

    **A**   ... a business uses their servers to store the files of an individual or another business.

    **B**   ... multiple users access a file at the same time.

*[1]*

**4.** A NIC is a piece of hardware that...

    **A**   ... allows a device to connect to a network.

    **B**   ... connects devices on a LAN.

    **C**   ... transmits data between networks.

*[1]*

**5.** The rules that govern how devices communicate and transmit data across a network are called...

    **A**   ... protocols.

    **B**   ... topologies.

    **C**   ... addresses.

*[1]*

**6.** Penetration testing is...

    **A**   ... investigating the cause of an attack on a network.

    **B**   ... detecting malware hidden within files downloaded from the Internet.

    **C**   ... identifying weaknesses in a network through simulated attacks.

*[1]*

**7.** Which one of these types of malware self-replicates?

    **A**   Worms

    **B**   Trojans

    **C**   Viruses

*[1]*

**8.** The TCP protocol...

    **A**   ... splits data into packets.

    **B**   ... encrypts information that is sent and received.

    **C**   ... is used to send emails.

*[1]*

**9.** What is a denial of service attack?

..................................................................................................................................

..................................................................................................................................

*[1]*

**10.** A company's network policy is shown on the right.
Give two further policies which could protect them.

> **Network Policy**
> • Use strong passwords
> • Regularly update anti-malware software

1. ...............................................................

..................................................................................................................................

2. ..................................................................................................................................

..................................................................................................................................

*[2]*

**11.** Why do packets sometimes arrive at the receiving device
in the wrong order and how are they reassembled?

..................................................................................................................................

..................................................................................................................................

..................................................................................................................................

*[2]*

**12.** Give two factors that can impact the performance of a wireless home network.

1. ..................................................................................................................................

..................................................................................................................................

2. ..................................................................................................................................

..................................................................................................................................

*[2]*

15

# Section 3: Issues

# Test 8

There are **12 questions** in this test. Give yourself **10 minutes** to answer them all.

**1.** Internet censorship is...

   **A** ... monitoring the websites that a user accesses on the Internet.

   **B** ... controlling what others can access and publish on the Internet.

*[1]*

**2.** True or False? "The Freedom of Information Act only covers digital records."

   **A** True

   **B** False

*[1]*

**3.** Can a for-profit company use a copyrighted photo on their website that is owned by someone else?

   **A** Yes, at any time.

   **B** Yes, with the owner's permission.

   **C** No, never.

*[1]*

**4.** Large amounts of E-waste is created as a result of people...

   **A** ... frequently upgrading to the latest electronic devices.

   **B** ... putting electronic devices into a sleep or hibernation mode.

*[1]*

**5.** Which of these is a valid reason for a company not to release any data they hold on a person under the Data Protection Act?

   **A** The company director refuses.

   **B** The data could affect a court case.

   **C** The data could damage the business.

*[1]*

**6.** A new online banking app could increase the profits of a bank. Which stakeholder(s) would be affected by the release of the app?

   **A** The customers of the bank.

   **B** The owners of the bank.

   **C** The customers and owners of the bank.

*[1]*

**7.** A person gains unauthorised access to a computer to steal data. This violates the...

   **A** ... Data Protection Act.

   **B** ... Computer Misuse Act.

   **C** ... Freedom of Information Act.

*[1]*

**8.** The Freedom of Information Act applies to...

   **A** ... public organisations only.

   **B** ... private businesses only.

   **C** ... both public organisations and private businesses.

*[1]*

**9.** What is a Creative Commons (CC) licence?

......................................................................................................................................

...................................................................................................................................... *[1]*

**10.** What is meant by the term 'cyberbullying'?

......................................................................................................................................

...................................................................................................................................... *[1]*

**11.** Give two ways that manufacturing a computer can negatively impact the environment.

1. ..................................................................................................................................

......................................................................................................................................

2. ..................................................................................................................................

...................................................................................................................................... *[2]*

**12.** A supermarket collects contact details from a customer to notify them of future offers. The data is stored on an unsecure server before being sold to a company, without the customer's permission, who uses the data to make unrelated sales calls.

Explain how this violates the Data Protection Act.

......................................................................................................................................

......................................................................................................................................

......................................................................................................................................

...................................................................................................................................... *[3]*

15

# Test 9

There are **11 questions** in this test. Give yourself **10 minutes** to answer them all.

1. Intellectual property is...

   A ... an original idea or piece of work that someone has created and belongs to them.

   B ... a type of legislation which protects copyrighted material.

   *[1]*

2. Why may a musician want to distribute their music under a Creative Commons licence?

   A To freely share their music without others needing to ask for permission.

   B To charge a fee if other people want to share their music.

   *[1]*

3. A cultural issue created by the Internet is that...

   A ... people can communicate more easily over large distances.

   B ... face-to-face social interactions can be neglected.

   *[1]*

4. In accordance with the Data Protection Act, how long should data be kept for?

   A Up to 25 years.

   B Only for as long as it is necessary.

   C There is no limit.

   *[1]*

5. Why might a government restrict access to certain websites?

   A To protect vulnerable members of the public, such as children.

   B To more easily collect data about website browsing habits.

   *[1]*

6. True of False? "Most organisations need to register with the government before they can begin collecting data."

   A True

   B False

   *[1]*

7. Devices consume large amounts of electricity. This has a negative effect on the environment because...

   A ... the majority of electricity is made from non-renewable energy resources.

   B ... producing electricity decreases the amount of pollution in the atmosphere.

   *[1]*

8. Which of the following is likely to consume the most energy?

   A A desktop computer on standby.

   B A smartphone charging.

   C A web server receiving a large amount of client requests.

   *[1]*

---

9.  What is meant by computer surveillance?

    ......................................................................................................................................

    ......................................................................................................................................

    *[1]*

10. Gareth lives in rural Wales and earns a low income.
    Why might he have limited access to technology?

    ......................................................................................................................................

    ......................................................................................................................................

    ......................................................................................................................................

    *[2]*

    What is the name given to the inequality created by people
    having different levels of access to technology?

    ......................................................................................................................................

    *[1]*

11. Give three examples of how technology can have
    a negative effect on a teenager's wellbeing.

    1. ..................................................................................................................................

    ......................................................................................................................................

    2. ..................................................................................................................................

    ......................................................................................................................................

    3. ..................................................................................................................................

    ......................................................................................................................................

    *[3]*

    <u>15</u>

# Test 10

There are **11 questions** in this test. Give yourself **10 minutes** to answer them all.

**1.** WPA2 is a type of encryption used to...

   **A**    ... secure Wi-Fi® networks.

   **B**    ... secure wired networks.

*[1]*

**2.** True or False? "The purpose of systems software is to run and maintain a computer system."

   **A**    True

   **B**    False

*[1]*

**3.** Which of the following generally has the lowest average capacity?

   **A**    SSD

   **B**    Memory card

   **C**    CD-ROM

*[1]*

**4.** Which part of the CPU holds the memory address for the next instruction to be processed?

   **A**    Memory Address Register (MAR)

   **B**    Accumulator

   **C**    Program Counter (PC)

*[1]*

**5.** Which is the correct description of flash memory?

   **A**    Solid state, non-volatile data storage

   **B**    Magnetic, volatile data storage

*[1]*

**6.** Which of the following types of malware disguises itself as legitimate software?

   **A**    Trojan

   **B**    Worm

   **C**    Virus

*[1]*

**7.** In which of the following scenarios would using cloud storage be most appropriate?

   **A**    A government organisation storing sensitive personal details.

   **B**    A small photography company with photographers working remotely.

   **C**    An author who has limited access to the Internet.

*[1]*

**8.** SMTP is used to...

   **A**    ... retrieve emails from a server.

   **B**    ... send emails and transfer them between servers.

   **C**    ... access websites and communicate with web servers.

*[1]*

**9.** Give two reasons why a star topology is often used on a LAN.

1. .............................................................................................................................

.............................................................................................................................

2. .............................................................................................................................

.............................................................................................................................

*[2]*

**10.** A virtual server is a software-based server that exists on a physical server.
Explain the environmental impact of using virtual servers
on a network instead of multiple physical servers.

.............................................................................................................................

.............................................................................................................................

.............................................................................................................................

.............................................................................................................................

*[2]*

**11.** Describe how a hard disk becomes fragmented.

.............................................................................................................................

.............................................................................................................................

.............................................................................................................................

.............................................................................................................................

Why is reading and writing slower when the hard disk is fragmented?

.............................................................................................................................

.............................................................................................................................

*[3]*

15

# Test 11

There are **11 questions** in this test.  Give yourself **10 minutes** to answer them all.

1.  An incremental backup...

    A  ... takes a copy of all files
       on a computer system.

    B  ... only copies files which
       have been created or edited
       since a previous backup.

    *[1]*

2.  Which of the following does an OS use
    to communicate with hardware?

    A  Device driver software

    B  Defragmentation software

    C  Graphical user interfaces

    *[1]*

3.  CPU performance depends on...

    A  ... clock speed, number
       of cores and cache size.

    B  ... clock speed, number
       of cores and bandwidth.

    C  ... number of cores, RAM capacity
       and number of USB ports.

    *[1]*

4.  Which of these is not a
    Data Protection Act principle?

    A  The rights of the data subject
       must be observed.

    B  Data must be accurate and up to date.

    C  Anyone can request data which is
       held by a public organisation.

    *[1]*

5.  A Virtual Private Network (VPN)...

    A  ... can be used to send data securely
       between two offices on different sites.

    B  ... will never share the same hardware
       as an existing physical network.

    *[1]*

6.  True or False?  "Privacy agreements can
    legally allow companies to target adverts
    at you using your personal information."

    A  True

    B  False

    *[1]*

7.  If a website has weak input validation,
    an SQL injection could...

    A  ... reveal sensitive information
       from a database.

    B  ... upgrade the database
       software version.

    *[1]*

8.  A hacker uses a packet sniffer to
    intercept and log traffic on a network.
    Which type of attack is this?

    A  Brute force

    B  Active

    C  Passive

    *[1]*

---

9. A restaurant introduces an app to take food orders.
   The app will be quicker at taking orders and cheaper than employing waiters.
   How will the restaurant's decision affect the following stakeholders?

   Waiters: .................................................................................................................

   ............................................................................................................................

   ............................................................................................................................

   Customers: ...........................................................................................................

   ............................................................................................................................

   ............................................................................................................................

   *[2]*

10. Describe how an OS manages memory and the CPU
    to run multiple applications at the same time.

    ............................................................................................................................

    ............................................................................................................................

    ............................................................................................................................

    ............................................................................................................................

    *[2]*

11. Tilly's computer is running slowly. Explain how upgrading
    the RAM could help to improve her computer's performance.

    ............................................................................................................................

    ............................................................................................................................

    ............................................................................................................................

    *[2]*

    Why might the upgrade have no effect on her computer's performance?

    ............................................................................................................................

    *[1]*

    15

# Test 12

There are **12 questions** in this test. Give yourself **10 minutes** to answer them all.

1. FTP is an example of a network protocol. What does FTP stand for?

   **A** Firmware Technology Protocol

   **B** File Transfer Protocol

   **C** Full Topology Protocol

   *[1]*

2. CAT 5e and CAT 6 are common types of...

   **A** ... coaxial cable.

   **B** ... fibre optic cable.

   **C** ... Ethernet cable.

   *[1]*

3. Which type of task is not handled by a computer's operating system?

   **A** Providing a user interface.

   **B** Managing user accounts.

   **C** Scanning packets entering the network for malware.

   *[1]*

4. Which of the following statements about external hard disk drives is true?

   **A** They have no moving parts.

   **B** They are portable.

   **C** They are unreliable.

   *[1]*

5. True or False? "A company is likely to own all of its WAN infrastructure."

   **A** True

   **B** False

   *[1]*

6. Which device initiates communication in a client-server network?

   **A** Client

   **B** Server

   *[1]*

7. The Basic Input Output System (BIOS) is stored in...

   **A** ... RAM.

   **B** ... ROM.

   **C** ... virtual memory.

   *[1]*

8. Which type of utility software may increase system performance after use?

   **A** Defragmentation software

   **B** Encryption software

   **C** Backup software

   *[1]*

---

9. A company's IT department uses the following backup routine.

| Monday-Saturday | Sunday |
|---|---|
| Incremental backup at 7 pm | Full system backup at 7 pm |

There was a large data loss at 3 pm on Tuesday.
How could the IT department restore as much of the lost data as possible?

..................................................................................................................................

..................................................................................................................................

*[1]*

10. Which part of the CPU holds the instruction or data
that has just been fetched from memory?

..................................................................................................................................

*[1]*

11. Give two criminal offences which were introduced with the Computer Misuse Act.

1. ...............................................................................................................................

..................................................................................................................................

2. ...............................................................................................................................

..................................................................................................................................

*[2]*

12. Explain how a brute force attack works and give
one way to reduce the risk of this type of attack.

..................................................................................................................................

..................................................................................................................................

..................................................................................................................................

..................................................................................................................................

*[3]*

15

# Test 13

There are **11 questions** in this test.  Give yourself **10 minutes** to answer them all.

1.  Blu-Ray discs can hold around...

    **A**  ... 250 MB of data.

    **B**  ... 2.5 GB of data.

    **C**  ... 25 GB of data.

    *[1]*

2.  Which type of memory is the fastest for the CPU to access?

    **A**  Cache

    **B**  Registers

    **C**  RAM

    *[1]*

3.  Which of the following network protocols is used to retrieve an email that is held on a server?

    **A**  HTTP

    **B**  SMTP

    **C**  POP3

    *[1]*

4.  Malware that monitors and sends a user's actions to a hacker is called...

    **A**  ... spyware.

    **B**  ... scareware.

    **C**  ... rootkit.

    *[1]*

5.  What is required to conduct network forensics on a network?

    **A**  DNA from an attacker left on a device.

    **B**  A way of recording all data that enters the network.

    **C**  CCTV footage of the building.

    *[1]*

6.  Which of the following protects new inventions, ideas and concepts, such as a new router design, from being duplicated?

    **A**  Copyright

    **B**  Creative Commons licences

    **C**  Patents

    *[1]*

7.  True or False?
    "It is possible to update the BIOS."

    **A**  True

    **B**  False

    *[1]*

8.  How many applications can be processed by a single core CPU at the same time?

    **A**  One

    **B**  Ten

    **C**  Unlimited

    *[1]*

**9.** What is a WAP used for?

..................................................................................................................................

..................................................................................................................................

[1]

**10.** Sort the following types of storage into the table below.

Magnetic Hard Disk, RAM, ROM, SSD, Magnetic Tape, Cache

| Primary Storage | Secondary Storage |
|---|---|
|  |  |
|  |  |
|  |  |

[2]

**11.** A company wants to develop an application to manage customer accounts.
Give two positives and two negatives of using an existing piece
of open source software as a starting point for their application.

Positives:

1. ................................................................................................................................

..................................................................................................................................

2. ................................................................................................................................

..................................................................................................................................

Negatives:

1. ................................................................................................................................

..................................................................................................................................

2. ................................................................................................................................

..................................................................................................................................

[4]

15

# Test 14

There are **12 questions** in this test. Give yourself **10 minutes** to answer them all.

1. What is needed to decrypt an encrypted file?

   **A**   A key

   **B**   A zip file

   **C**   An external hard drive

   *[1]*

2. The main memory of a computer is its...

   **A**   ... RAM.

   **B**   ... internal hard drive.

   **C**   ... virtual memory.

   *[1]*

3. Which of the following types of cable is typically the most expensive?

   **A**   Ethernet

   **B**   Coaxial

   **C**   Fibre Optic

   *[1]*

4. True or False? "Members of the public can request specific information held by public organisations."

   **A**   True

   **B**   False

   *[1]*

5. Network protocols operate on different layers. These layers...

   **A**   ... overlap each other.

   **B**   ... are independent of each other.

   *[1]*

6. Each core in a multi-core CPU processes data...

   **A**   ... together with the other cores.

   **B**   ... separately from the other cores.

   *[1]*

7. Which type of attack stops users accessing a website by flooding the network with large amounts of useless traffic?

   **A**   Denial of service

   **B**   Brute force

   **C**   SQL injection

   *[1]*

8. Which of the following is usually the weakest point in a computer network?

   **A**   Anti-virus software

   **B**   The users of the system

   **C**   Physical security (padlocks, CCTV, locked doors, etc.)

   *[1]*

9. What happens if a receiving device on a TCP/IP network does not receive all packets within a certain time?

.......................................................................................................................

.......................................................................................................................

*[1]*

10. Why is secondary storage not affected during a power cut?

.......................................................................................................................

.......................................................................................................................

*[1]*

11. Suggest three ways to reduce the risk of health problems when using a computer.

1. ...................................................................................................................

.......................................................................................................................

2. ...................................................................................................................

.......................................................................................................................

3. ...................................................................................................................

.......................................................................................................................

*[3]*

12. Give one benefit and one drawback of using a GUI instead of a command line interface.

Benefit: ............................................................................................................

.......................................................................................................................

Drawback: .........................................................................................................

.......................................................................................................................

*[2]*

15

# Section 4: Algorithms

 **Test 15**

There are **8 questions** in this test. Give yourself **10 minutes** to answer them all.

**1.** What is the first step of the linear search algorithm?

   **A**    Identify the middle item in the list.

   **B**    Look at the first item in the list.

   **C**    Split the list in half.

*[1]*

**2.** Ignoring any information about a problem that isn't important is called...

   **A**    ... decomposition.

   **B**    ... abstraction.

*[1]*

**Questions 3 – 6 are on the following flow diagram.**

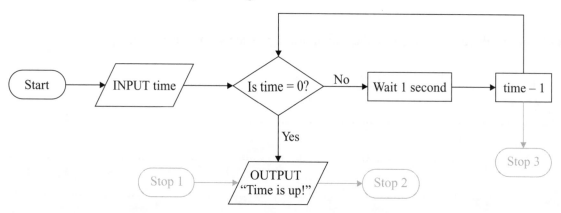

**3.** Which Stop box correctly completes the flow diagram?

   **A**    Stop 1

   **B**    Stop 2

   **C**    Stop 3

*[1]*

**4.** The flow diagram shows...

   **A**    ... iteration only.

   **B**    ... selection only.

   **C**    ... selection and iteration.

*[1]*

**5.** What does the flow diagram represent?

   **A**    A clock

   **B**    A stopwatch

   **C**    A countdown

*[1]*

**6.** What command does the diamond box represent in the flow diagram?

   **A**    Decision

   **B**    Sub routine

   **C**    Process

*[1]*

7. Put the following words into alphabetical order using the insertion sort algorithm.

Orange, Kiwi, Pear, Banana, Apple

...........................................................................................................................................

...........................................................................................................................................

...........................................................................................................................................

...........................................................................................................................................

...........................................................................................................................................

*[4]*

8. Balthazar's Bookshop calculates an employee's monthly pay using the algorithm below.

```
01  totalHours = input("Enter the number of hours worked")
02  totalPay = totalHours * 9
```

Describe what each line of code does.

Line 01: ...........................................................................................................................

.............................................................................................................................................

Line 02: ...........................................................................................................................

.............................................................................................................................................

*[2]*

If at least £10,000 of stock is sold in a month, employees now receive a £50 bonus.
Complete the flow diagram below to calculate and output an employee's new
monthly pay. The sub routine PAY represents the algorithm described above.

Start ⟶ | PAY |                                        Stop

*[3]*   | 15 |

# Test 16

There are **9 questions** in this test. Give yourself **10 minutes** to answer them all.

1.  Which of the following search algorithms can only be carried out on an ordered list?

    **A**   Linear search

    **B**   Binary search

    *[1]*

2.  Computational thinking is used to…

    **A**   … improve the efficiency of an existing program or piece of code.

    **B**   … turn a problem into something a computer can help you solve.

    *[1]*

3.  A programmer solves a complex task by writing many small sub programs. This is an example of…

    **A**   … decomposition.

    **B**   … abstraction.

    **C**   … authentication.

    *[1]*

4.  An online dictionary uses a program to sort a very large list of unordered words into alphabetical order. Which sorting algorithm would sort the list most efficiently?

    **A**   Bubble sort

    **B**   Insertion sort

    **C**   Merge sort

    *[1]*

**Questions 5 and 6 are on the following algorithms.**

**Algorithm 1**
```
litres = input("Enter the number of litres")
pints = litres * 1.76
print(pints)
```

**Algorithm 2**
```
Take the number of litres and convert it
into pints and then print that answer
```

5.  A benefit of using Algorithm 1 over Algorithm 2 is that...

    **A**   … it can be more easily converted into a programming language.

    **B**   … it can be interpreted by all programming languages.

    *[1]*

6.  An issue with Algorithm 2 is that...

    **A**   … it does not use the proper syntax of a programming language.

    **B**   … it is vague and unstructured.

    *[1]*

**7.** Give two advantages of using an insertion sort.

1. ..............................................................................................................................

..............................................................................................................................

2. ..............................................................................................................................

..............................................................................................................................

[2]

**8.** Use a bubble sort to put the following numbers in ascending order,
while showing the order at the end of each pass: 7, 12, 14, 2, 8

..............................................................................................................................

..............................................................................................................................

..............................................................................................................................

..............................................................................................................................

..............................................................................................................................

..............................................................................................................................

[3]

**9.** A film streaming website uses an algorithm to restrict which films a user can view.
Draw a flow diagram to show this algorithm. Your flow diagram should:
- Have one input for the user's age and one input for the age rating of a film.
- Allow or deny access depending on whether the user is old enough to view the film.

[4]

15

# Section 5: Programming

# Test 17

There are **9 questions** in this test. Give yourself **10 minutes** to answer them all.

**1.** A procedure...

   **A** ... always takes at least one parameter.

   **B** ... never returns a value.

*[1]*

**2.** True or False? "Records can only contain values which are all of the same data type."

   **A** True

   **B** False

*[1]*

**3.** Which of the following data types could store the value 45.31?

   **A** Integer

   **B** Real

   **C** Boolean

*[1]*

**4.** Which expression evaluates to TRUE?

   **A** `3 < 5 AND 1 > 2`

   **B** `1 != 1 OR 4 < 5`

   **C** `NOT(7 > 3)`

*[1]*

**Questions 5 and 6 are on the following table and SQL statement.**

| Table: seatingPlan | | | | |
|---|---|---|---|---|
| ID | firstName | lastName | dateOfBirth | seatNum |
| 1 | Humza | Ahmed | 08/02/1993 | 4B |
| 2 | Janet | Swan | 13/12/1986 | 13K |
| 3 | Ollie | Fisher | 29/05/1996 | 24A |
| 4 | Agata | Kowalski | 10/03/1990 | 7D |

```
SELECT firstName, dateOfBirth FROM seatingPlan WHERE lastName LIKE "%r"
```

**5.** What will the SQL statement above return?

   **A**

| Humza | 08/02/1993 |
|---|---|

   **B**

| Fisher | 29/05/1996 |
|---|---|

   **C**

| Ollie | 29/05/1996 |
|---|---|

*[1]*

**6.** Which SQL statement would return all records in the table?

   **A** `SELECT ID FROM seatingPlan`

   **B** `SELECT * FROM seatNum`

   **C** `SELECT * FROM seatingPlan`

*[1]*

**7.** What is meant by casting?

...................................................................................................................................

*[1]*

**8.** The formula for triangle number $n$ is $0.5\,n\,(n+1)$.  Complete the algorithm below to write the first 10 triangle numbers to a text file called 'output.txt' and close the file.

```
01  nums = openWrite(.................................................................)

02  n = 1

03  while n < .......................

04  value = 0.5 * n * (n + 1)

05      .......................................................................

06      n = n + 1

07  endwhile

08  .......................................................................
```

*[4]*

**9.** The array `scoresArch` holds the scores of five archers in a competition. `scoreArch[1, 2]` contains the value 8.

Write a line of pseudocode to insert a score of 7 into the empty element in the array.

|  |  | Archer | | | | |
|---|---|---|---|---|---|---|
|  |  | **0** | **1** | **2** | **3** | **4** |
| **Shot** | **0** | 5 | 3 | 10 | 6 | 8 |
|  | **1** | 3 | 1 | 8 | 7 | 7 |
|  | **2** | 4 | 1 | 9 | 10 |  |

...................................................................................................................................

*[1]*

Write a function that takes the array and an archer number as parameters and returns an archer's total score.

*[3]*

```
15
```

Section 5: Programming

# Test 18

There are **11 questions** in this test. Give yourself **10 minutes** to answer them all.

**1.** What will `23 DIV 4` return?

   **A** 6

   **B** 3

   **C** 5

*[1]*

**2.** True or False? "The value of a constant can't be modified whilst a program is running."

   **A** True

   **B** False

*[1]*

**Questions 3 and 4 are on the following array.**

```
01  . . . . . . . . . . . . . .
02  goals[0, 0] = 5
03  goals[0, 1] = 11
04  goals[1, 0] = 4
05  goals[1, 1] = 7
```

**3.** Which line of code is missing from line 01?

   **A** `array goals[2, 2]`

   **B** `array goals[1, 1]`

   **C** `array goals[0, 2]`

*[1]*

**4.** Why is it appropriate to store this data in an array?

   **A** No data uses the string data type.

   **B** All the data is of the same data type.

*[1]*

**5.** Which of these commands is required first when reading data from a file?

   **A** `readLine()`

   **B** `openRead()`

   **C** `writeLine()`

*[1]*

**6.** Parameters are…

   **A** … types of variable used to pass information into a sub program.

   **B** … the actual information that is passed into a sub program.

*[1]*

**7.** What does `ASC("c")` do?

   **A** Returns the ASCII code for the character "c".

   **B** Returns TRUE if "c" is in the ASCII character set.

*[1]*

**8.** A program deploys the rear wing of a supercar when the variable `speed` is greater than 70. Which of the following would be the most appropriate in this program?

   **A** An IF statement.

   **B** A SWITCH-CASE statement.

*[1]*

---

Section 5: Programming

9. A user registers on a website with the details on the right.

State the output of the following lines of code:

```
firstName = "John"
lastName = "Jones"
age = "34"
```

`print(firstName.subString(3,1))` ......................................................

`print(lastName.length + age.length)` ......................................................

`print(lastName.subString(3,2).upper)` ......................................................

*[3]*

10. An electronic safe requires a 5 digit code to open. A program will deny all access to the safe as soon as an incorrect digit is entered. Suggest, with a reason, whether IF-ELSEIF statements or nested IF statements are more appropriate for this program.

......................................................................................................

......................................................................................................

*[2]*

11. The table `flightPaths` shows information about flights from UK airports.

| Table: flightPaths | | | |
|---|---|---|---|
| flightNumber | depAirport | destAirport | depTime |
| AA442 | Manchester | New York | 09:45 |
| A7757 | Liverpool | Las Vegas | 11:33 |
| F142 | Liverpool | Menorca | 08:30 |
| KL114 | Heathrow | Edinburgh | 16:42 |

Write an SQL statement to return:

the flight number and destination of all flights departing from Liverpool.

......................................................................................................

......................................................................................................

*[1]*

the departure airport and time of all flights whose flight number ends in 2.

......................................................................................................

......................................................................................................

*[1]*

15

# Test 19

There are **9 questions** in this test. Give yourself **10 minutes** to answer them all.

1. Which operator is used to raise a number to a power?

   A   DIV

   B   ^

   C   MOD

   *[1]*

2. Given that x = "CompSci" and test = x.subString(4,1), what is the output of print(test)?

   A   S

   B   p

   C   Comp

   *[1]*

**Questions 3 to 6 are on the following program.**

```
int playerScore
highScore = 89
playerScore = input("Please enter your score")
if playerScore < 1 OR playerScore > 100 then
    print("Invalid score entered")
elseif playerScore > highScore then
    print("New high score, well done!")
elseif playerScore < highScore then
    print("You did not beat the high score")
else
    print("You equalled the high score!")
endif
```

3. playerScore is declared as an integer. Using the correct data type makes the code...

   A   ... less memory efficient.

   B   ... more robust.

   *[1]*

4. The flow of the program is controlled using...

   A   ... a selection statement.

   B   ... an iteration statement.

   C   ... both selection and iteration statements.

   *[1]*

5. Which of these inputs would result in the output Invalid score entered?

   A   67

   B   100

   C   101

   *[1]*

6. What would the program output if playerScore = 90?

   A   You equalled the high score!

   B   New high score, well done!

   C   You did not beat the high score

   *[1]*

---

Section 5: Programming

© CGP — not to be photocopied

**7.** Explain the difference between the = operator and the == operator.

..........................................................................................................................................

..........................................................................................................................................

*[2]*

**8.** Why is it suitable to use the string data type to store a postcode?

..........................................................................................................................................

..........................................................................................................................................

*[1]*

**9.** Mike has written three procedures:
   1. `listUsers()`    2. `createUser()`    3. `deleteUser()`

Write an algorithm using a SWITCH-CASE statement which:
- asks a user to input a number and runs the matching procedure,
  e.g. an input of 2 runs the `createUser` procedure.
- displays a message if an input has no matching procedure.

*[4]*

Mike defines a local variable in the `listUsers` procedure.
He later tries to reuse the variable outside of the procedure. Explain what will happen.

..........................................................................................................................................

..........................................................................................................................................

*[2]*

$\boxed{15}$

# Test 20

There are **9 questions** in this test. Give yourself **10 minutes** to answer them all.

1. Does NOT(8 != 11) evaluate to TRUE or FALSE?

   A   TRUE

   B   FALSE

   *[1]*

2. Which of the following is a count-controlled loop?

   A   FOR loop

   B   WHILE loop

   C   DO WHILE loop

   *[1]*

**Questions 3 to 6 are on the following program.**

```
01 real radiation = x  //x is the radiation measured in the facility.
02 int temp = t  //t is the temperature of the reactor.
03 do
04   if temp > 320 then
05     deployCoolant()  //activates procedure to cool the reactor.
06   endif
07   print("Radiation level at" + " " + str(radiation))
08   warningSiren = FALSE
09 while radiation < 0.35
10 warningSiren = TRUE  //plays a warning siren around the facility.
11 print("Evacuate the facility now!")
```

3. Why is casting needed in line 07?

   A   There are more than two strings being concatenated.

   B   radiation is real but needs to be concatenated with a string.

   *[1]*

4. The DO WHILE loop checks the value of radiation at the end of the loop. Which other type of loop also checks a condition at the end?

   A   WHILE

   B   DO UNTIL

   *[1]*

5. Which of the following statements is true?

   A   The value of radiation determines whether a warning siren plays.

   B   The value of temp determines which message is printed.

   *[1]*

6. If 0.4 is the amount of radiation measured in the facility, what is the first string that would be output by the program?

   A   Evacuate the facility now!

   B   Radiation level at 0.4

   *[1]*

**7.** What two pieces of information are given to a field in a record?

1. ...........................................................................................................................

2. ...........................................................................................................................

*[2]*

**8.** The words below are stored in an array called `pets[]`.

| rex | summer | fudge | mickey | rebel |
|-----|--------|-------|--------|-------|

Complete the algorithm to change the contents of the array to all uppercase.

```
01  i = 0
02  do
03      pets[i] = ............................................................
04      i = i + 1
05  until i == ......................................
```

*[2]*

Explain the effect of deleting line 04.

.........................................................................................................................................

.........................................................................................................................................

*[2]*

**9.** Write a function called `average` which takes three integer parameters and returns their average. Only the whole number part of the average should be returned.

*[3]*

15

# Test 21

There are **12 questions** in this test.  Give yourself **10 minutes** to answer them all.

1.  A program only allows users to input an integer between 0 and 10. This is an example of...

    **A**   ... input diagnostics.

    **B**   ... input validation.

    *[1]*

2.  A good test plan should...

    **A**   ... outline what will be tested and how it will be tested.

    **B**   ... only test for one potential way a user may misuse a program.

    *[1]*

3.  A program creates a default password based on the age of a user.  Which of the following test data for the program is not erroneous?

    **A**   4£

    **B**   64

    **C**   –28

    *[1]*

4.  Which of these is not a part of defensive design?

    **A**   Anticipating how a program may be used incorrectly in the future.

    **B**   Authenticating users of a program to prevent unauthorised access.

    **C**   Encrypting a program so it cannot be deciphered.

    *[1]*

5.  True or False?  "All assembly languages are compatible with all CPU types."

    **A**   True

    **B**   False

    *[1]*

6.  Iterative testing takes place...

    **A**   ... during development.

    **B**   ... after development is complete.

    *[1]*

7.  An assembler converts...

    **A**   ... machine code into assembly language.

    **B**   ... assembly language into high-level language.

    **C**   ... assembly language into machine code.

    *[1]*

8.  Which of these is a valid way of reducing the number of characters in a program without compromising its functionality?

    **A**   Removing all indentation.

    **B**   Renaming all variables as single letters ("a", "b", "c" etc.)

    **C**   Replacing repeated code with functions or procedures.

    *[1]*

9.  What is a logic error?

    ...........................................................................................................................................

    ...........................................................................................................................................
    *[1]*

10. Describe a feature of an IDE which can be used to identify logic errors.

    ...........................................................................................................................................

    ...........................................................................................................................................
    *[1]*

11. A compiler and an interpreter are two types of translators.
    What is the purpose of a translator?

    ...........................................................................................................................................

    ...........................................................................................................................................
    *[1]*

    Describe the main difference between a compiler and an interpreter.

    ...........................................................................................................................................

    ...........................................................................................................................................

    ...........................................................................................................................................
    *[2]*

12. Why is it important to keep code well-maintained?

    ...........................................................................................................................................

    ...........................................................................................................................................

    ...........................................................................................................................................

    ...........................................................................................................................................
    *[2]*

    ┌──────┐
    │  ——  │
    │  15  │
    └──────┘

44

# Test 22

There are **10 questions** in this test. Give yourself **10 minutes** to answer them all.

1. True or False? "Testing is essential to find any logic errors within code."

   A True

   B False

   *[1]*

2. Which of these translators will stop when they reach the first error in a program?

   A Compiler

   B Interpreter

   *[1]*

3. A program can be made more robust by using...

   A ... global variables where possible.

   B ... local variables where possible.

   C ... an equal amount of local and global variables.

   *[1]*

4. Which part of an IDE may include automatic features to format comments?

   A Run-time environment

   B Breakpoints

   C Code editor

   *[1]*

5. Which of the following low-level languages is easier for programmers to code in?

   A Assembly language

   B Machine code

   *[1]*

6. Error diagnostic tools...

   A ... can identify syntax errors in code and give the location of the errors.

   B ... auto-correct any logic errors in code and give the location of the errors.

   *[1]*

7. Asking a user to enter a username and password is a type of...

   A ... validation.

   B ... encryption.

   C ... authentication.

   *[1]*

8. A software company is developing a program for an embedded system with limited memory. Which type of language would be most appropriate to write in?

   A High-level language

   B Low-level language

   *[1]*

---

Section 6: Design, Testing and IDEs

**9.** Kaira needs to create an email address. Give two input validation checks that may be used to check her email address is in an acceptable format.

1. ...........................................................................................................................................

2. ...........................................................................................................................................

*[2]*

**10.** The program below takes an input and returns a student's grade.

```
01  int number
02  number = input("Please enter your mark")
03  total = 80
04  percentage = number/total * 100
05  if (percentage >= 70 AND percentage <= 100) then
06  print("You have achieved a grade A")
07  elseif (percentage >= 50 AND percentage < 70) then
08  print("You have achieved a grade B")
09  elseif (percentage >= 30 AND percentage < 50) then
10  print("You have achieved a grade C")
11  else
12  print("You have failed")
13  endif
```

Give two ways, using examples from the code, how the maintainability of the program could be improved.

1. ...........................................................................................................................................

2. ...........................................................................................................................................

*[2]*

Complete the following test plan for the program by filling in the missing entries.

| Type of data | Test data | Reason for testing | Actual Outcome |
|---|---|---|---|
| | 40 | | "You have achieved a grade C" |
| | 90 | To ensure the program can handle incorrect inputs. | |
| Extreme | 80 | | |

*[3]*

15

Section 6: Design, Testing and IDEs

# Test 23

There are **11 questions** in this test. Give yourself **10 minutes** to answer them all.

1.  Which of these units of data is the largest?

    A   Gigabyte

    B   Megabyte

    C   Terabyte

    *[1]*

2.  Which of the following denary values represents the hexadecimal character "E"?

    A   15

    B   13

    C   14

    *[1]*

3.  Unicode® is a character set which has characters for...

    A   ... all major languages.

    B   ... the English language only.

    *[1]*

4.  Bit rate is calculated using the formula...

    A   ... sampling frequency ÷ sample size

    B   ... sampling frequency × sample size

    C   ... sampling frequency + sample size

    *[1]*

5.  Which of the following binary numbers represents the denary value 33?

    A   00100001

    B   01000001

    C   00010001

    *[1]*

6.  Which logic gate gives an output of 1, if either input is 1?

    A   AND gate

    B   NOT gate

    C   OR gate

    *[1]*

7.  How many characters are in the ASCII character set?

    A   64

    B   128

    C   256

    *[1]*

8.  Pixels are...

    A   ... small dots that make up a bitmap image.

    B   ... pieces of information that contain an image's file format, colour depth, etc.

    *[1]*

9. Add the binary numbers 01010101 and 01101101.

[2]

10. Explain what is meant by 'overflow'.

..........................................................................................................

..........................................................................................................

..........................................................................................................

..........................................................................................................

[2]

11. A photographer wants to compress some high-quality images so they can be stored on an external hard drive, while maintaining the quality of the images.

Which type of compression should the photographer use?

..........................................................................................................

[1]

Explain why this type of compression is the most appropriate for the photographer.

..........................................................................................................

..........................................................................................................

..........................................................................................................

..........................................................................................................

[2]

15

# Test 24

There are **10 questions** in this test. Give yourself **10 minutes** to answer them all.

1. A one place left shift on a binary number...

   A   ... doubles the number.

   B   ... halves the number.

   *[1]*

2. All data must be converted into...

   A   ... a binary format to be processed by a computer.

   B   ... a hexadecimal format to be processed by a computer.

   *[1]*

3. How many bits are in a kilobyte?

   A   8000

   B   1000

   C   4

   *[1]*

4. True or False? "An image's creation date, time and location are all types of metadata."

   A   True

   B   False

   *[1]*

5. Which of these hexadecimal numbers is the largest?

   A   23

   B   1F

   C   2A

   *[1]*

6. The process of converting an analogue signal to a digital signal is known as...

   A   ... compression.

   B   ... re-coding.

   C   ... sampling.

   *[1]*

7. Hexadecimal numbers are often used by programmers instead of binary numbers because...

   A   ... there are fewer hexadecimal numbers than binary numbers.

   B   ... they are shorter, which makes them easier to remember.

   *[1]*

8. Increasing the number of bits used for each pixel in an image will...

   A   ... increase the range of colours that the image can display.

   B   ... decrease the resolution of the image.

   C   ... have no effect on the file size.

   *[1]*

9. Complete the following truth table.

| A | B | C | A AND B | NOT C | X = (A AND B) OR (NOT C) |
|---|---|---|---|---|---|
| 0 | 0 | 0 | | 1 | |
| 0 | 0 | 1 | | 0 | |
| 0 | 1 | 0 | | 1 | |
| 0 | 1 | 1 | | 0 | |
| 1 | 0 | 0 | | 1 | |
| 1 | 0 | 1 | | 0 | |
| 1 | 1 | 0 | | 1 | |
| 1 | 1 | 1 | | 0 | |

*[2]*

Draw the logic circuit for X = (A AND B) OR (NOT C).

*[3]*

10. A singer is recording the vocal tracks for their new album.
A sound engineer increases the sampling frequency and sampling
size of the recordings. Outline the benefit of both these changes.

Sampling frequency: ........................................................................................................

..................................................................................................................................

Sampling size: ...............................................................................................................

..................................................................................................................................

*[2]*

15

50

There are **11 questions** in this test.  Give yourself **10 minutes** to answer them all.

1.  How many bits are in a nibble?

    **A**  2

    **B**  4

    **C**  8

    *[1]*

2.  A hexadecimal digit can represent...

    **A**  ... 2 different values.

    **B**  ... 10 different values.

    **C**  ... 16 different values.

    *[1]*

3.  What is 00100111 as a denary number?

    **A**  43

    **B**  39

    **C**  78

    *[1]*

4.  Decreasing the sampling interval...

    **A**  ... increases the sampling frequency.

    **B**  ... increases the bit rate.

    **C**  ... increases both the sampling frequency and the bit rate.

    *[1]*

5.  Which of the following character sets can represent the most characters?

    **A**  ASCII

    **B**  Extended ASCII

    **C**  Unicode®

    *[1]*

6.  An audio file has an average size of 4 MB. How much storage space would 1000 of these files take up?

    **A**  4 gigabytes

    **B**  4 petabytes

    **C**  40 000 bytes

    *[1]*

7.  Which of the following denary values is equal to the hex value FF?

    **A**  15

    **B**  128

    **C**  255

    *[1]*

8.  Which logic gate gives an output of 0, if both inputs are 0?

    **A**  AND gate

    **B**  OR gate

    **C**  Both AND and OR gates

    *[1]*

---

Section 7: Data Representation

**9.** The function shiftR takes an 8-bit binary number and performs a 4 place right shift.
State what the following would return:

shiftR(00110000) ............................................................................

shiftR(11011001) ............................................................................

*[2]*

The function shiftR is used to divide numbers by 16.
Outline why shiftR(11011001) returns an answer with a loss of accuracy.

......................................................................................................

......................................................................................................

*[1]*

**10.** Claire has received a compressed version of a file in an email.
Why has compression been used on this file?

......................................................................................................

......................................................................................................

......................................................................................................

......................................................................................................

*[2]*

**11.** An odd parity bit adds a 1 to the end of a binary string if it has an even
number of 1s or a 0 if the binary string has an odd number of 1s.

Add an odd parity bit to the binary string 1011100.

......................................................................................................

*[1]*

Explain how an odd parity bit can detect errors.

......................................................................................................

......................................................................................................

*[1]*

15

# Mixed Tests for Paper 2

## Test 26

There are **11 questions** in this test. Give yourself **10 minutes** to answer them all.

---

**1.** In order to halve a binary number, all bits are...

   **A**  ... shifted 1 place to the left.

   **B**  ... shifted 1 place to the right.

   **C**  ... shifted 2 places to the right.

*[1]*

**2.** True or False? "Input sanitisation involves checking input data and modifying it before passing it into a program."

   **A**  True

   **B**  False

*[1]*

**3.** Combining two string variables is called...

   **A**  ... concentration.

   **B**  ... coordination.

   **C**  ... concatenation.

*[1]*

**4.** Which of the following data amounts is the largest?

   **A**  400 MB

   **B**  0.3 GB

   **C**  8000 KB

*[1]*

**5.** A list has 4 items. What is the maximum number of comparisons needed to sort the list using an insertion sort?

   **A**  4

   **B**  6

   **C**  8

*[1]*

**6.** When testing a program, extreme data should be used to...

   **A**  ... test that the program can handle invalid inputs.

   **B**  ... test that the program accepts inputs at the limit of what it should be able to handle.

*[1]*

**7.** Developing a logical set of instructions to solve a particular problem is known as...

   **A**  ... abstraction.

   **B**  ... decomposition.

   **C**  ... algorithmic thinking.

*[1]*

**8.** The bit rate of an audio file is the number of bits...

   **A**  ... available for each sample.

   **B**  ... processed per second.

*[1]*

---

**9.** Which set of input values will give an output of 1 in the logic circuit below?

Input A ──────────┐

Output R

Input B ──▷o──────┘

A = ................., B = .................
*[1]*

Write the logic statement for the logic circuit.

R = ...................................................................
*[1]*

**10.** All guests of a hotel must rate their stay on a scale from 1 to 5 when checking out.
Write some pseudocode to:
- ask a guest to enter their name and a rating (1, 2, 3, 4 or 5).
- output a message that thanks the guest with their name if a valid input is entered.
- output an appropriate message if an invalid input is entered.

*[3]*

**11.** Explain how global variables can sometimes cause problems in large
programs and why local variables are often preferred by developers.

.............................................................................................................

.............................................................................................................

.............................................................................................................

.............................................................................................................
*[2]*

15

# Test 27

There are **10 questions** in this test. Give yourself **10 minutes** to answer them all.

1. How many unique colours can a 4-bit image use?

   **A**  8

   **B**  16

   **C**  24

   *[1]*

2. Which of the following is an example of a logic error?

   **A**  A DIV operator is used instead of a MOD operator.

   **B**  A function is called but a bracket is missing.

   *[1]*

**Questions 3 – 6 are on the following table and SQL statement.**

| Table: boats | | | | |
|---|---|---|---|---|
| make | model | engine_type | radar_fitted | engine_size |
| Swift | Racer | Petrol | False | 2.5 |
| June | Spirit | Petrol | False | 1.4 |
| Swift | Ranger | Diesel | True | 2.0 |
| Ocean Crawler | Enterprise | Diesel | True | 1.6 |

```
SELECT _____ FROM boats WHERE engine_size < 1.6
```

3. Which of these statements is correct?

   **A**  Each row of the table is an array.

   **B**  Each row of the table is a record.

   *[1]*

4. What field name is missing from the SQL statement above if 'Spirit' is returned?

   **A**  engine_size

   **B**  model

   **C**  engine_type

   *[1]*

5. Which data type is most appropriate for the field radar_fitted?

   **A**  String

   **B**  Character

   **C**  Boolean

   *[1]*

6. What is appropriate input sanitisation to use on the field engine_size?

   **A**  Remove any decimal points.

   **B**  Remove any digits.

   **C**  Remove any letters.

   *[1]*

**7.** Convert the binary number 10101110 into hexadecimal.

........................................................................................................................................

........................................................................................................................................

*[2]*

**8.** Convert the denary number 142 into hexadecimal.

........................................................................................................................................

........................................................................................................................................

*[2]*

**9.** A merge sort is being carried out on the following letters:  Z C G A L B T F
The algorithm has already split the list so that each letter is in its own list.
Complete the algorithm to put the letters in alphabetical order.

*[3]*

**10.** Give two benefits of a programmer using a high-level language
rather than a low-level language.

1. ........................................................................................................................................

........................................................................................................................................

2. ........................................................................................................................................

........................................................................................................................................

*[2]*

15

**Test 28**

There are **11 questions** in this test.  Give yourself **10 minutes** to answer them all.

1.  Which of the following
    statements evaluates to 2?

    **A**  `11 MOD 3`

    **B**  `10/3`

    **C**  `3 DIV 2`

    *[1]*

2.  Which type of flow diagram box is
    a rectangle with rounded corners?

    **A**  Sub Routine

    **B**  Start/Stop

    **C**  Decision

    *[1]*

3.  What would the logic statement
    `33 > 10 OR 5 < 3` evaluate to?

    **A**  TRUE

    **B**  FALSE

    *[1]*

4.  A collection of characters that a
    computer recognises from their
    binary representation is called a...

    **A**  ... font.

    **B**  ... character set.

    *[1]*

5.  A developer wants to compress some
    software to send to a client.  Which
    type of compression cannot be used?

    **A**  Lossy

    **B**  Lossless

    *[1]*

6.  How many possible combinations of inputs
    are there for a logic circuit with 3 inputs?

    **A**  8

    **B**  10

    **C**  9

    *[1]*

7.  Which of these would not make a password-
    based authentication system more secure?

    **A**  Enforce users to change their
    password every month.

    **B**  Enforce users to use no numbers
    or symbols in a password.

    *[1]*

8.  Which of the following
    is equal to 1 petabyte?

    **A**  1000 terabytes

    **B**  1000 gigabytes

    **C**  1000 bytes

    *[1]*

**9.** A record structure has been defined on the right.

```
record lakes
   int lakeNum
   str lakeName
   real maxDepth
   bool boatsAllowed
endrecord
```

Explain why the following line of code would return an error:
`lake1 = lakes(2, "Ulls", sixty, true)`

...........................................................................................................

...........................................................................................................

*[2]*

**10.** Describe two features of an IDE that can make writing a program easier.

1. ...........................................................................................................

...........................................................................................................

2. ...........................................................................................................

...........................................................................................................

*[2]*

**11.** The text file 'mass.txt' on the right shows the masses of five objects.
A scientist wants to write a program to analyse these values.

Write some pseudocode that reads each value from 'mass.txt' and puts
them into a different element of an array called `data`.
Your program must contain a FOR loop.

**mass.txt**

| |
|---|
| 332.1 |
| 461.4 |
| 74.1 |
| 24.6 |
| 100.0 |

*[3]*

15

**Test 29**

There are **9 questions** in this test. Give yourself **10 minutes** to answer them all.

1. A program that compiles successfully but does something unexpected when it is running contains...

    **A**   ... syntax errors.

    **B**   ... logic errors.

    [1]

2. Which logic gate only takes a single input?

    **A**   NOT

    **B**   AND

    **C**   OR

    [1]

3. What is the denary value of the binary number 00100011?

    **A**   19

    **B**   35

    **C**   36

    [1]

4. Which of these lines of code does not use a comparison operator?

    **A**   x = 9 * 8

    **B**   y == 10

    **C**   z > 7

    [1]

**Questions 5 and 6 are on the following flow diagram.**

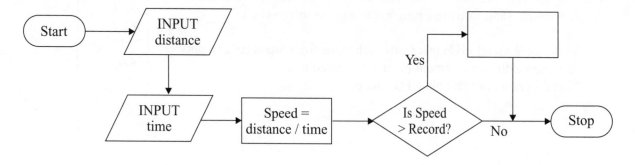

5. Which programming construct is used at the diamond box?

    **A**   Selection

    **B**   Sequence

    **C**   Iteration

    [1]

6. Which of these commands should be used in the empty box to update Record?

    **A**   Record = Speed

    **B**   Speed = Record

    **C**   Record = Record + Speed

    [1]

7.  Convert the hexadecimal number 4F into denary.

    ......................................................................................................................................

    ......................................................................................................................................
    *[2]*

8.  A student decides to only test their application at the end of development.
    Explain why this could cause problems for the student.

    ......................................................................................................................................

    ......................................................................................................................................

    ......................................................................................................................................
    *[2]*

9.  The sales array holds the sales of a shop for each day of the week.
    For example, sales[0] holds the sales for Monday.
    Write a DO UNTIL loop to calculate weekSales, the total sales for the week.

    *[3]*

    The weekly profit is calculated by subtracting the variables
    weekSalaries and weekRent from weekSales.
    Write a function with three parameters to return the weekly profit.

    *[2]*

    $\dfrac{\phantom{xx}}{15}$

# Test 30

There are **11 questions** in this test. Give yourself **10 minutes** to answer them all.

1. An audio file needs to be compressed. Which of these formats would give a higher quality audio file?

   **A**  MP3 (a lossy format)

   **B**  FLAC (a lossless format)

   *[1]*

2. Which of the following statements would evaluate to TRUE when a = 49?

   **A**  `a > 49 AND a < 49`

   **B**  `a >= 50 OR a <= 75`

   **C**  `a != 49`

   *[1]*

3. True or False? "Defensive design involves anticipating how a user may misuse a program."

   **A**  True

   **B**  False

   *[1]*

4. Given that `cityName = "Liverpool"`. Which function would output `"erp"`?

   **A**  `cityName.subString(3,3)`

   **B**  `cityName.String(3,5)`

   **C**  `cityName.subString(4,3)`

   *[1]*

5. An algorithm written in pseudocode...

   **A**  ... should always use the proper syntax of a programming language.

   **B**  ... can show the same solution to a problem that a flow diagram can.

   *[1]*

6. What are breakpoints used for in an IDE?

   **A**  To show lines of code that don't have any comments.

   **B**  To provide syntax highlighting.

   **C**  To pause the program on specific lines to allow for further investigation.

   *[1]*

7. A PDF file of a 200 page textbook is likely to contain...

   **A**  ... 40 bytes of data.

   **B**  ... 40 terabytes of data.

   **C**  ... 40 megabytes of data.

   *[1]*

8. A binary search is performed on a list of 5 items. What is the greatest number of comparisons needed to find an item?

   **A**  2

   **B**  3

   **C**  4

   *[1]*

**9.** Complete the truth table below.

| A | B | A ∧ B | ¬ (A ∧ B) |
|---|---|---|---|
| False | False | | |
| False | True | | |
| True | False | | |
| True | True | | |

*[2]*

**10.** The program below counts the number of prizes left in a competition.

```
01  beachprize = 100
02  skiprize = 50
03  code = input("Enter a code for a chance to win!")
04  switch type:
05      case "Beach108":
06          beachprize = beachprize - 1
07          print("You have won a beach prize!")
08      case "Ski209":
09          skiprize = skiprize - 1
10          print("You have won a ski prize!"
11      case default:
12          print("You have not won this time!")
```

Identify three errors in this program.

1. ...........................................................................................................................

2. ...........................................................................................................................

3. ...........................................................................................................................

*[3]*

**11.** Explain a disadvantage of increasing the resolution of an image.

..............................................................................................................................

..............................................................................................................................

..............................................................................................................................

*[2]*

15

# Answers

## Section 1: Components of a Computer System

### Test 1 — Pages 2–3
1. C *[1 mark]*
2. A *[1 mark]*
3. B *[1 mark]*
4. C *[1 mark]*
5. A *[1 mark]*
6. A *[1 mark]*
7. A *[1 mark]*
8. B *[1 mark]*
9. E.g. dishwasher / microwave / TV / washing machine *[1 mark]*
10. Compressing the file will reduce the size of the file, so it will take up less storage space / will be quicker to transfer over the Internet *[1 mark]*.
11. Full backups take a copy of every file on a system *[1 mark]*. Incremental backups only copy the files that have been created/edited since the last backup *[1 mark]*.
12. E.g. The Control Unit sends signals to load the address of the program counter into the MAR *[1 mark]*. The data/instruction in that memory address is then fetched from memory and stored in the MDR *[1 mark]*. The PC is incremented to point to the address of the next instruction *[1 mark]*.

### Test 2 — Pages 4–5
1. B *[1 mark]*
2. B *[1 mark]*
3. B *[1 mark]*
4. B *[1 mark]*
5. C *[1 mark]*
6. C *[1 mark]*
7. A *[1 mark]*
8. C *[1 mark]*
9. To process data and instructions to make a computer system function correctly *[1 mark]*.
10. Any two from: e.g. Provide a user interface. / Handle file and disk management. / Manage user accounts and security. / Control the CPU and memory resources. *[2 marks]*
11. Any two advantages: e.g. The SSD will not require defragmenting. / The SSD will withstand shocks better than the HDD. / The SSD is silent. *[2 marks]*

    Any two disadvantages: e.g. The SSD is likely to cost more than the HDD. / The SSD is likely to have a lower capacity than the SSD. / The SSD has a shorter read/write life and will deteriorate over time. *[2 marks]*

### Test 3 — Pages 6–7
1. B *[1 mark]*
2. A *[1 mark]*
3. A *[1 mark]*
4. C *[1 mark]*
5. A *[1 mark]*
6. B *[1 mark]*
7. A *[1 mark]*
8. C *[1 mark]*
9. It can make a computer slow to respond when switching between applications or performing memory-intensive tasks *[1 mark]*.
10. The accumulator stores intermediate results of calculations performed by the ALU *[1 mark]*.
11. Any two from: e.g. Password / PIN / User-access levels / Fingerprint scanner / Retina scanner *[2 marks]*
12. E.g. USB Flash Drive *[1 mark]*

    Any two from: e.g. USB flash drives offer appropriate storage capacity for the files. / They are small and portable. / They are robust and unlikely to get damaged. / Most laptops have USB ports, so it is appropriate for students. *[2 marks]*

## Section 2: Networks

### Test 4 — Pages 8–9
1. A *[1 mark]*
2. A *[1 mark]*
3. B *[1 mark]*
4. C *[1 mark]*
5. B *[1 mark]*
6. B *[1 mark]*
7. C *[1 mark]*
8. B *[1 mark]*
9. Star topology *[1 mark]*
10. E.g. A weak password is easier to guess, so his account could be broken into via a brute force attack *[1 mark]*. The anti-malware software may not detect newer versions of malware attempting to be installed *[1 mark]*.
11. Any two advantages: e.g. Files can be accessed from any device with Internet access. / Security and backups are provided. / Saves space on hard drives, reducing the need to buy larger hard drives. *[2 marks]*

    Any two disadvantages: e.g. Files cannot be accessed without an Internet connection. / Reliant on the cloud host to ensure data is secure. / Possible legal issues regarding the ownership of data stored. / Subscription fees can be expensive in the long term. *[2 marks]*

### Test 5 — Pages 10–11
1. C *[1 mark]*
2. B *[1 mark]*
3. A *[1 mark]*
4. B *[1 mark]*
5. B *[1 mark]*
6. C *[1 mark]*
7. A *[1 mark]*
8. B *[1 mark]*
9. To check that the packet has not been corrupted during transit *[1 mark]*.
10. E.g. It is many characters in length *[1 mark]*. / It contains a mixture of letters and symbols etc. *[1 mark]*.
11. E.g. Company A has IT specialists which could install and update all employees' software at the same time in a client-server network *[1 mark]*. It will be easier to keep track of and backup files as they are stored centrally *[1 mark]*.

    Company B has no IT specialists. A peer-to-peer network would be easy to set up and maintain *[1 mark]* and wouldn't require any expensive hardware or IT specialists *[1 mark]*.

### Test 6 — Pages 12–13
1. B *[1 mark]*
2. A *[1 mark]*
3. B *[1 mark]*
4. C *[1 mark]*
5. C *[1 mark]*
6. A *[1 mark]*
7. B *[1 mark]*
8. C *[1 mark]*
9. HTTPS / HTTP Secure / Hyper Text Transfer Protocol Secure *[1 mark]*
10. User access levels control which parts of a network that different groups of users can and cannot access *[1 mark]*.
11. A virtual network is a network that is mainly software based *[1 mark]*. It is created by partitioning off some of a physical network's bandwidth *[1 mark]*.
12. Any three from: e.g. Files can be shared easily. / Devices such as printers can be shared across the business. / Devices can share an Internet connection. / Employees can log on to their accounts from any device on the network. *[3 marks]*

### Test 7 — Pages 14–15
1. A *[1 mark]*
2. B *[1 mark]*
3. A *[1 mark]*
4. A *[1 mark]*
5. A *[1 mark]*
6. C *[1 mark]*
7. A *[1 mark]*
8. A *[1 mark]*

# Answers

9. A DoS attack is where someone tries to stop users accessing part of a network or website by flooding a network with traffic *[1 mark]*.
10. Any two from: e.g. Pentest the network regularly. / Enforce user access levels to limit access to sensitive data. / Use firewalls. / Encrypt all sensitive data. *[2 marks]*
11. Packets can take different routes through a network causing them to arrive in the wrong order *[1 mark]*. Packets are reassembled in the right order by the receiving device using the packet numbers *[1 mark]*.
12. Any two from: e.g. Number of devices connected to the network. / High-bandwidth activities, such as streaming or online gaming. / The position of the home router (due to interference from obstacles such as walls). / Interference from other nearby wireless networks on adjacent channels. *[2 marks]*

## Section 3: Issues
### Test 8 — Pages 16–17
1. B *[1 mark]*  2. B *[1 mark]*
3. B *[1 mark]*  4. A *[1 mark]*
5. B *[1 mark]*  6. C *[1 mark]*
7. B *[1 mark]*  8. A *[1 mark]*
9. A licence that allows people to legally share media and software without having to ask permission, provided they follow certain conditions *[1 mark]*.
10. Cyberbullying is when somebody uses social media to deliberately harm somebody else *[1 mark]*.
11. E.g. Manufacturing requires large amounts of energy, which creates pollution *[1 mark]*. Large amounts of raw materials are used *[1 mark]*.
12. E.g. The Data Protection Act gives certain rights to customers which aren't being considered by the supermarket *[1 mark]*. E.g. the data is not being used for it's specified purpose *[1 mark]*, and is being used in an unlawful way *[1 mark]*.

### Test 9 — Pages 18–19
1. A *[1 mark]*  2. A *[1 mark]*
3. B *[1 mark]*  4. B *[1 mark]*
5. A *[1 mark]*  6. A *[1 mark]*
7. A *[1 mark]*  8. C *[1 mark]*
9. Computer surveillance is when someone monitors what people are doing on their computers *[1 mark]*.
10. He is likely to live in an area with poor reception quality and broadband speed *[1 mark]*. He may not be able to afford new technology with his low income *[1 mark]*.

    The digital divide *[1 mark]*.
11. E.g. Teenagers can experience cyberbullying or trolling on social media sites *[1 mark]*. / Teenagers may come across inappropriate material or be at risk of exploitation on the Internet *[1 mark]*. / Teenagers are pressured into always having the latest device by their peers *[1 mark]*.

## Mixed Tests for Paper 1
### Test 10 — Pages 20–21
1. A *[1 mark]*  2. A *[1 mark]*
3. C *[1 mark]*  4. C *[1 mark]*
5. A *[1 mark]*  6. A *[1 mark]*
7. B *[1 mark]*  8. B *[1 mark]*
9. Any two from: e.g. If a device fails or is disconnected, the rest of the network is unaffected. / It is easy to add new devices to the network. / Data goes straight to the central device, reducing the chance for data collisions. *[2 marks]*
10. E.g. Multiple virtual servers run on one physical server, so less energy is used compared to having multiple physical servers *[1 mark]*. Fewer physical servers have to be built, so fewer natural resources are used up *[1 mark]*.
11. Gaps on a hard disk appear when files are moved, deleted or change size *[1 mark]*. New files are saved in different gaps *[1 mark]*.

    The read/write head has to move back and forth across the disk as fragmented files are not stored together *[1 mark]*.

### Test 11 — Pages 22–23
1. B *[1 mark]*  2. A *[1 mark]*
3. A *[1 mark]*  4. C *[1 mark]*
5. A *[1 mark]*  6. A *[1 mark]*
7. A *[1 mark]*  8. C *[1 mark]*
9. Waiters: e.g. they could lose their jobs *[1 mark]*. Customers: e.g. they will have faster service *[1 mark]*.
10. The OS manages memory resources so that applications do not interfere with each other *[1 mark]*. The OS divides CPU time between open applications, prioritising certain processes, so that instructions are executed efficiently *[1 mark]*.
11. She would have higher capacity/ speed in primary storage *[1 mark]*, so the CPU could have quicker access to more data *[1 mark]*.

    If she has sufficient RAM for her needs, more RAM may have no effect on performance *[1 mark]*.

### Test 12 — Pages 24–25
1. B *[1 mark]*  2. C *[1 mark]*
3. C *[1 mark]*  4. B *[1 mark]*
5. B *[1 mark]*  6. A *[1 mark]*
7. B *[1 mark]*  8. A *[1 mark]*
9. They should restore Sunday's full backup, followed by Monday's incremental backup *[1 mark]*.
10. Memory Data Register *[1 mark]*
11. Any two from: Gaining unauthorised access to a private network or device through hacking. / Accessing a network or device in order to commit a crime. / Purposefully spreading malware. *[2 marks]*
12. E.g. Hackers will use trial and error to guess a password *[1 mark]*. They use software to try different passwords very quickly *[1 mark]*. A way to reduce the risk of this attack is by locking an account after a certain number of attempts *[1 mark]*.

### Test 13 — Pages 26–27
1. C *[1 mark]*  2. B *[1 mark]*
3. C *[1 mark]*  4. A *[1 mark]*
5. B *[1 mark]*  6. C *[1 mark]*
7. A *[1 mark]*  8. A *[1 mark]*
9. A WAP allows devices to connect wirelessly to a LAN *[1 mark]*.

# 64

# Answers

10.

| Primary Storage | Secondary Storage |
| --- | --- |
| RAM | Magnetic Hard Disk |
| ROM | SSD |
| Cache | Magnetic Tape |

*[2 marks for all correct, 1 mark for any four answers sorted correctly]*

11. Positives: e.g. Open source software is often free, reducing development cost *[1 mark]*. / It can be modified to fit the company's needs *[1 mark]*.

Negatives: e.g. Open source software may not get regular updates, which leads to bugs etc. *[1 mark]*. / There is limited user documentation, making it harder to learn *[1 mark]*.

## Test 14 — Pages 28–29

1. A *[1 mark]*    2. A *[1 mark]*
3. C *[1 mark]*    4. A *[1 mark]*
5. B *[1 mark]*    6. B *[1 mark]*
7. A *[1 mark]*    8. B *[1 mark]*
9. It sends a timeout message to the sending device *[1 mark]*.
10. Secondary storage is non-volatile, so retains data without power *[1 mark]*.
11. E.g. Take regular breaks *[1 mark]*. / Sit with a correct posture *[1 mark]*. / Sit a reasonable distance from the screen *[1 mark]*.
12. Benefit: e.g. A GUI is more intuitive and interactive than a command line interface *[1 mark]*.
Drawback: e.g. A GUI uses more resources than a command line interface *[1 mark]*.

## Section 4: Algorithms

### Test 15 — Pages 30–31

1. B *[1 mark]*    2. B *[1 mark]*
3. B *[1 mark]*    4. C *[1 mark]*
5. C *[1 mark]*    6. A *[1 mark]*
7. Orange, <u>Kiwi</u>, Pear, Banana, Apple
Kiwi, Orange, <u>Pear</u>, Banana, Apple
Kiwi, Orange, Pear, <u>Banana</u>, Apple
Banana, Kiwi, Orange, Pear, <u>Apple</u>
Apple, Banana, Kiwi, Orange, Pear
*[1 mark for each row from rows 2-5]*
8. Line 01: asks user to input number of hours worked and assigns input to the variable *totalHours [1 mark]*.
Line 02: multiplies the input from Line 01/*totalHours* by 9 *[1 mark]*.

E.g.

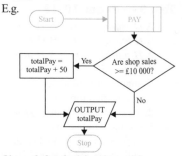

*[1 mark for decision box with appropriate question, 1 mark for calculating new total pay, 1 mark for output]*

## Test 16 — Pages 32–33

1. B *[1 mark]*    2. B *[1 mark]*
3. A *[1 mark]*    4. C *[1 mark]*
5. A *[1 mark]*    6. B *[1 mark]*
7. Any two from: e.g. They can handle small lists very efficiently. / They are very memory efficient as all sorting is done in the original list. / They can quickly check if a list is already sorted. *[2 marks]*
8. First pass: 7, 12, 2, 8, 14 *[1 mark]*
Second pass: 7, 2, 8, 12, 14 *[1 mark]*
Third pass: 2, 7, 8, 12, 14 *[1 mark]*
Fourth pass: no swaps, list is ordered.
9. E.g.

```
Start
INPUT user's age
INPUT film age-rating
Is user's age ≥ film age-rating?
  Yes → Allow user to watch film → Stop
  No → Don't allow user to watch film → Stop
```

*[1 mark for start and stop, 1 mark for input boxes, 1 mark for decision box with appropriate question, 1 mark for process boxes]*

## Section 5: Programming

### Test 17 — Pages 34–35

1. B *[1 mark]*    2. B *[1 mark]*
3. B *[1 mark]*    4. B *[1 mark]*
5. C *[1 mark]*    6. C *[1 mark]*

7. Casting converts one data type to a different data type *[1 mark]*.
8. 01   *nums = openWrite("output.txt")*
   03   *while n < 11*
   05     *nums.writeLine(value)*
   08   *nums.close()*
   *[1 mark for each correct line]*
9. *scoresArch[2,4] = 7 [1 mark]*

E.g.
*function totalScore(scoresArch, arch)*
  *total = 0*
  *for i = 0 to 2*
    *total = total + scoresArch[i, arch]*
  *next i*
  *return total*
*endfunction*
*[1 mark for defining a function with two parameters, 1 mark for calculating total, 1 mark for returning total]*

## Test 18 — Pages 36–37

1. C *[1 mark]*    2. A *[1 mark]*
3. A *[1 mark]*    4. B *[1 mark]*
5. B *[1 mark]*    6. A *[1 mark]*
7. A *[1 mark]*    8. A *[1 mark]*
9. "n" *[1 mark]*
   7 *[1 mark]*
   "ES" *[1 mark]*
10. E.g. Nested IF statements are more appropriate *[1 mark]* as they will only check the next digit of the code if the previously entered digit is correct *[1 mark]*.
11. *SELECT flightNumber, destAirport FROM flightPaths WHERE depAirport = "Liverpool" [1 mark]*

*SELECT depAirport, depTime FROM flightPaths WHERE flightNumber LIKE "%2" [1 mark]*

## Test 19 — Pages 38–39

1. B *[1 mark]*    2. A *[1 mark]*
3. B *[1 mark]*    4. A *[1 mark]*
5. C *[1 mark]*    6. B *[1 mark]*
7. = assigns a value to a variable *[1 mark]*, whereas == compares values/variables and returns TRUE if they match *[1 mark]*.
8. A postcode contains numbers and letters, which can be stored as a string *[1 mark]*.

# Answers

9. E.g.
*userSelect = input("Choose option")*
*switch userSelect:*
  *case 1:*
    *listUsers()*
  *case 2:*
    *createUser()*
  *case 3:*
    *deleteUser()*
  *default:*
    *print("Unrecognised selection")*
*endswitch*
**[1 mark for a user input, 1 mark for use of case statements, 1 mark for correct procedures, 1 mark for printing message for "default" case]**

Local variables cannot be used outside of the procedure **[1 mark]**. He will get an error as the variable is not defined elsewhere **[1 mark]**.

## Test 20 — Pages 40–41

1. B **[1 mark]**    2. A **[1 mark]**
3. B **[1 mark]**    4. B **[1 mark]**
5. A **[1 mark]**    6. B **[1 mark]**
7. Data type **[1 mark]**
   Field name **[1 mark]**
8. 03   *pets[i] = pets[i].upper*
   05   *until i == 5*
   **[1 mark for each correct line]**

   As *i* would not increase, the DO UNTIL loop would run indefinitely **[1 mark]** and would only change "rex" to upper case **[1 mark]**.
9. E.g.
   *function average(a, b, c)*
     *total = a + b + c*
     *ans = total DIV 3*
     *return ans*
   *endfunction*
   **[1 mark for defining a function with three parameters, 1 mark for finding the average, 1 mark for returning the whole number part]**

## Section 6: Design, Testing and IDEs

## Test 21 — Pages 42–43

1. B **[1 mark]**    2. A **[1 mark]**
3. B **[1 mark]**    4. C **[1 mark]**
5. B **[1 mark]**    6. A **[1 mark]**
7. C **[1 mark]**    8. C **[1 mark]**

9. When a compiler/interpreter is able to run a program, but it doesn't behave as expected **[1 mark]**.
10. E.g. Breakpoints can be used to stop the program at specific points to allow a programmer to check things like the values of variables **[1 mark]**.
11. To convert a programming language into machine code **[1 mark]**.

    A compiler translates all of the source code at the same time to create a single executable file **[1 mark]**, whereas an interpreter translates the source code one instruction at a time (and does not create an executable file) **[1 mark]**.
12. E.g. to make it easy to read and modify **[1 mark]**. It also allows other programmers to understand what your program does **[1 mark]**.

## Test 22 — Pages 44–45

1. A **[1 mark]**    2. B **[1 mark]**
3. B **[1 mark]**    4. C **[1 mark]**
5. A **[1 mark]**    6. A **[1 mark]**
7. C **[1 mark]**    8. B **[1 mark]**
9. E.g. Check it has an @ symbol and a .com or .co.uk **[1 mark]**. / Check it has fewer than a certain number of characters **[1 mark]**.
10. Any two from: e.g. A comment could be added to line 05 to explain what the IF-ELSEIF statement does. / Indentation could be used inside the IF-ELSEIF statement to make the flow of the program easier to identify. / The variable name "mark" could be used instead of "number" to make it clear what the variable is being used for. **[2 marks]**

First row
Type: Normal
Reason: To ensure the program can handle a correct input.
Second row
Type: Erroneous
Outcome: "You have failed"
Third row
Reason: To ensure the program can handle the largest input value.
Outcome: "You have achieved a grade A"
**[1 mark for each correct row]**

## Section 7: Data Representation

## Test 23 — Pages 46–47

1. C **[1 mark]**    2. C **[1 mark]**
3. A **[1 mark]**    4. B **[1 mark]**
5. A **[1 mark]**    6. C **[1 mark]**
7. B **[1 mark]**    8. A **[1 mark]**
9.    0 1 0 1 0 1 0 1
    + 0 1 1 0 1 1 0 1
    ‾‾‾‾‾‾‾‾‾‾‾‾‾‾‾‾‾‾
      1 1 0 0 0 0 1 0
      ₁ ₁ ₁ ₁ ₁   ₁
    **[1 mark for working, 1 mark for correct answer]**
10. Overflow is when a calculation **[1 mark]** produces an answer that has more bits than the CPU was expecting **[1 mark]**.
11. Lossless compression **[1 mark]**.

    Data is temporarily removed from the image, which is then restored when the image is opened **[1 mark]**. Therefore, the photographer can recover the original high-quality image as no data is lost **[1 mark]**.

## Test 24 — Pages 48–49

1. A **[1 mark]**    2. A **[1 mark]**
3. A **[1 mark]**    4. A **[1 mark]**
5. C **[1 mark]**    6. C **[1 mark]**
7. B **[1 mark]**    8. A **[1 mark]**
9.

| A AND B | NOT C | X |
|---------|-------|---|
| 0 | 1 | 1 |
| 0 | 0 | 0 |
| 0 | 1 | 1 |
| 0 | 0 | 0 |
| 0 | 1 | 1 |
| 0 | 0 | 0 |
| 1 | 1 | 1 |
| 1 | 0 | 1 |

**[1 mark for each correct column]**

Input A
Input B
Input C
Output X

**[1 mark for correct AND gate, 1 mark for correct NOT gate, 1 mark for an OR gate with output X]**
10. The number of samples taken each second increases, so the digital sound file is closer to the original vocals **[1 mark]**. Quieter sounds are picked up, so the digital sound file is closer to the original vocals **[1 mark]**.

66

# Answers

## Test 25 — Pages 50–51
1. B *[1 mark]*  2. C *[1 mark]*
3. B *[1 mark]*  4. C *[1 mark]*
5. C *[1 mark]*  6. A *[1 mark]*
7. C *[1 mark]*  8. C *[1 mark]*
9. 00000011 *[1 mark]*
   00001101 *[1 mark]*

   shiftR(11011001) returns an answer where the '1001' bits have been lost, so the fractional part of the division would not be included *[1 mark]*.
10. E.g. Compression makes the file smaller in size *[1 mark]*, so it will be faster to upload and send via email *[1 mark]*.
11. 10111001 *[1 mark]*

   An error is detected if a string is read and it has an even number of 1s *[1 mark]*.

## Mixed Tests for Paper 2
### Test 26 — Pages 52–53
1. B *[1 mark]*  2. A *[1 mark]*
3. C *[1 mark]*  4. A *[1 mark]*
5. B *[1 mark]*  6. B *[1 mark]*
7. C *[1 mark]*  8. B *[1 mark]*
9. A = 1, B = 0 *[1 mark]*
   R = A AND (NOT B) *[1 mark]*
10. E.g.
    ```
    string name
    int rating
    name = input("Enter your name")
    rating = input("Enter your rating")
    if rating >= 1 AND rating <= 5 then
      print("Thank you " + name)
    else
      print("Invalid rating entered")
    endif
    ```
    *[1 mark for user inputs, 1 mark for a selection statement, 1 mark for printing a correct message depending on input]*
11. If a variable is global then you need to be careful that you don't change it or use the same name somewhere else in the program *[1 mark]*. Local variables can only be used inside a sub program, so developers can use them without risk of changing other parts of the main program *[1 mark]*.

## Test 27 — Pages 54–55
1. B *[1 mark]*  2. A *[1 mark]*
3. B *[1 mark]*  4. B *[1 mark]*
5. C *[1 mark]*  6. C *[1 mark]*
7. Split into nibbles: 1010, 1110. 1010 = A and 1110 = E *[1 mark]* So 10101110 is AE in hex *[1 mark]*
8. 142 ÷ 16 = 8 remainder 14 *[1 mark]* 14 is E in hexadecimal, so 142 is 8E in hexadecimal *[1 mark]*
9. Merge and order sub-lists until there is one list:
   CZ  AG  BL  FT *[1 mark]*
   ACGZ  BFLT *[1 mark]*
   ABCFGLTZ *[1 mark]*
10. Any two benefits: e.g. Easier for programmers to read and understand. / A single instruction of high-level code can represent many low-level instructions. / A programmer does not need to have knowledge about the internal structure of the CPU to write high-level code. / High-level code can work on multiple machines with different processors. *[2 marks]*

## Test 28 — Pages 56–57
1. A *[1 mark]*  2. B *[1 mark]*
3. A *[1 mark]*  4. B *[1 mark]*
5. A *[1 mark]*  6. A *[1 mark]*
7. B *[1 mark]*  8. A *[1 mark]*
9. The *maxDepth* field has the real data type *[1 mark]*. *sixty* can't be stored as this data type, so an error would be returned *[1 mark]*.
10. E.g. A code editor can have auto-colour coding, auto-indent etc. to help readability. / A run-time environment can quickly run code within an IDE and show where any errors take place. *[2 marks]*
11. E.g.
    ```
    array data[5]
    values = openRead("mass.txt")
    for i = 0 to 4
      data[i] = values.readLine()
    next i
    values.close()
    ```
    *[1 mark for opening file in read mode and closing file, 1 mark for use of readLine(), 1 mark for a correct FOR loop]*

## Test 29 — Pages 58–59
1. B *[1 mark]*  2. A *[1 mark]*
3. B *[1 mark]*  4. A *[1 mark]*
5. A *[1 mark]*  6. A *[1 mark]*
7. $(4 \times 16) = 64$ and F = 15, *[1 mark]* so 4F = 64 + 15 = 79 *[1 mark]*
8. E.g. It is likely that the app will have many errors in its code *[1 mark]*. Any serious errors may be time-consuming to fix and could delay the release of the app *[1 mark]*.
9. E.g.
   ```
   weekSales = 0
   i = 0
   do
     weekSales = weekSales + sales[i]
     i = i + 1
   until i == 6
   ```
   *[1 mark for a correct DO UNTIL loop, 1 mark for correct UNTIL condition, 1 mark for correctly calculating weekSales]*
   ```
   function profit(weekRent, weekSalaries, weekSales)
     tCost = weekRent + weekSalaries
     weekProfit = weekSales – tCost
     return weekProfit
   endfunction
   ```
   *[1 mark for a function with three parameters, 1 mark for returning a correctly calculated weekly profit]*

## Test 30 — Pages 60–61
1. B *[1 mark]*  2. B *[1 mark]*
3. A *[1 mark]*  4. A *[1 mark]*
5. B *[1 mark]*  6. C *[1 mark]*
7. C *[1 mark]*  8. B *[1 mark]*
9.

| $A \wedge B$ | $\neg (A \wedge B)$ |
| --- | --- |
| False | True |
| False | True |
| False | True |
| True | False |

*[1 mark for each column]*
10. Line 04: *switch type* should be *switch code* *[1 mark]*. Line 10: there is a missing closed bracket *[1 mark]*. There is no line of code to end the SWITCH-CASE statement *[1 mark]*.
11. The size of the image file will increase *[1 mark]*, so it will require more storage space *[1 mark]*.